THE

IN THE

By MICHAEL HULETT

© Copyright, 1982, by Michael Hulett

9780907926214

HANBURY PLAYS

PIONE~~~~   KEEPER'S LODGE   ~, INC.
BROUGHTON GREEN
DROITWICH
WORCESTERSHIRE WR9 7EE

THE WIND IN THE WILLOWS

Cast of Characters

TOAD

an irrepressible, irresponsible gadabout. Proud, wealthy and infectiously good-natured.

RAT

a practical, dependable chap. Methodical, even-tempered and only slightly stuffy.

MOLE

a shy and affectionate friend. Near-sighted, but wide-eyed with wonder, curious and loyal.

BADGER

a wise but stern authoritarian. Old-fashioned, stalwart and kind.

JUDGE

a pompous autocrat, easily riled.

WASHERWOMAN

a poor but generous soul.

ENGINEER

a stong-minded but tolerant railway man.

THIEF

a somewhat dashing and less-than-somewhat competent brigand.

NOTE: The roles of the JUDGE, WASHERWOMAN, ENGINEER and THIEF, all humans, may be played by the same actor. All roles may be played equally well by men or women.

SYNOPSIS OF SCENES/MUSICAL NUMBERS

Scene 1   The Prologue   "The Wind In The Willows"

Scene 2   The River Bank   "Life On The River"

                              "The Open Road"

Scene 3   The Open Road

Scene 4   The Court   "The Great and Glorious Toad"

Scene 5   Rat's House

Scene 6   The Prison

Scene 7   The Wild Wood   "Home"

Scene 8   The Railway   "The Railroad Track"

Scene 9   The Wild Wood   "The Piper At The Gates Of Dawn"

Scene 10   The Campfire

Scene 11   Toad Hall

SETTING

(Refer to Production Notes Page 32)

THE WIND IN THE WILLOWS

Scene One
The Prologue

AT RISE: Sounds of the forest; chirps, whistles, hoots, croaks, made by the actors backstage. Music. MOLE ENTERS, either through the audience or under the curtain. MOLE strolls through the Audience, singing and speaking to Audience Members as if they were the animals of the forest.

MOLE: *(Sings: "The Wind In The Willows".)*
    Can you hear what I hear?
    The whisper and swish of the wind in the willows
        down by the shallows,
    Calling me.
    The creak of the crickets in fields lying fallow,
    Sunburnt and yellow.
    Can you see?
(Speaks.) Hello, Chipmunk. Hello, Rabbit. How are you, Miss Possum? It is a beautiful day for Autumn, isn't it? Oh, listen. *(Sings.)*
    Can you hear what I hear?
    The buzz as the bees swarm in trees that are hollow,
    Humming like cellos loud and harsh.
    The belch of the bullfrogs who bask as they bellow,
    While they all wallow in the marsh.
(Speaks.) Hello there, Mr. Owl. Did I wake you up? Have you seen Rat? How do you do, little Bluebird. My name is Mole. Very pleased to meet you, I'm sure. *(Sings.)*
    Can you hear what I hear?
    The tweet and the twitter of sparrows and swallows,
    Music that's mellow and it's free.
    The squirrels and the chipmunks, such chattering fellows:
    Good morning hellos from a tree. *(Speaks.)*
You all smell very fine. I can tell just by sniffing that you're friends. I'm sorry I can't see you better. We moles are very short-sighted, you know. That comes from spending so much time underground. I can hardly see past the tip of my nose. How many toes do you see? Three? *(Bringing his paw to his nose.)* You're right. It's a good thing my nose is so good. Why, I can find an ant in a field of clover, just by his smell. Without my nose I could hardly get around. Only last week I had a cold in my nose and I was in terrible trouble. I would have gotten lost but for the fact that I can hear almost as well as I can smell. I love the sounds of the forest. As long as I can hear you Chipmunks or you

1

Goldfinches or you Butterflies I know right where I am, and which way is home. For instance, do you know what the willow trees sound like with wind in their branches? Sh-h-h-h. *(Actors backstage supplement each sound.)* When I hear that I'm near the riverbank. The bees tell me I'm by the old hollow tree. That's why I sing my song: *(Sings.)*
    Can you hear what I hear?
    The whisper and swish of the wind in the willows.
(Speaks.) Come on. Help me out. Make the sound of the willows. Sh-h-h-h-h. *(Sings.)*
    Can you hear what I hear?
    The buzzing of bees by the tree standing hollow.
(Speaks.) You know what bees sound like. Bz-zz-zz-zz. Pretend you're bees. Yes, that's very fine. *(Sings.)*
    Can you hear what I hear?
    The tweet and the twitter of sparrows and swallows.
(MOLE whistles.) That's lovely. I feel so at home. What did you say? Rat is suspecting me? Oh, Rat is expecting me. Let's look in on him, shall we?

Scene Two
The River Bank

Curtain opens. RAT is sitting idly with a picnic basket beside him. He is gazing dreamily toward the Audience. The edge of the stage will represent the bank of the river. MOLE joins RAT. MOLE often tries to imitate RAT'S gestures.

MOLE: Hello, Rat.
RAT: Hello, Mole.
MOLE: Am I late?
RAT: Nonsense. Who could possibly be late on a day as fine as today?
MOLE: It is a lovely day.
RAT: As always.
MOLE: The sun feels warm on my fur and the breeze is cool on my nose. It's so pleasant here by the river.
RAT: As always.
MOLE: *(Sniffs.)* The river smells like . . . like butterscotch pudding with plum sauce.
RAT: No, that's lunch. I brought a few things in the basket.
MOLE: Oh, may I unpack it please, Ratty? I'd so enjoy it.
RAT: Well, if you insist.

MOLE: *(Dropping the basket with a loud crash.)* Oh, dear!
(Peering inside.) Tell me, Ratty, do you like horseradish sand-
wiches soaked in pickle juice? I'm afraid I've made a mess of
lunch.

RAT: Quite all right, Mole. I suppose I wasn't really hungry.
Is there a chance for tea?

MOLE: *(Peering again.)* No. Sorry.

RAT: Ah, well.

MOLE: Are you terribly angry with me?

RAT: No, no. You didn't mean it. Nothing will spoil the
beauty of the day nor the harmony of the river. Let's just
sit back and enjoy it, eh?

MOLE: All right. *(But MOLE is restless.)* What lies over
there? Beyond the river?

RAT: That? Oh, that's just the Wild Wood. *(Handing MOLE
a spyglass from basket.)* We don't go there very much, we
river-bankers.

MOLE: Aren't they . . . aren't they very nice animals in there?

RAT: Nice isn't the word. They're a different sort in there
where it's dark at midday and cold in July. Snakes and
weasels and vultures and bears. Stay out of their way and
you'll stay out of their stomachs. And then there's Badger,
of course. He lives right in the heart of it; wouldn't live
anywhere else, either, though don't ask me why. Dear old
Badger! Nobody interferes with him. They'd better not!

MOLE: And beyond the Wild Wood again? Where it's all blue
and dim, and one sees what may be hills and something like
the smoke of a great many gray fires.

RAT: Beyond the Wild Wood comes the Wide World. And
that's something that has nothing to do with us, nor we with
it. The Wide World is where people live. Human people.
I've never been there, and I'm not going, nor you either, if
you have any sense about you. Don't ever refer to it again,
please.

MOLE: What are human people like? I've never seen one up
close, which is to say I've never seen one at all.

RAT: My dear friend, difficult as it may be, you try my
patience. The Good Lord who watches over all animals
never intended such a day for so many questions.

MOLE: Sorry.

RAT: Think no more about it.

MOLE: I can't help thinking about things. There's so much to
wonder.

RAT: *(Yawning.)* Ah, life!

MOLE: What?

RAT: Ah, the river.

MOLE: I thought you said, "Ah, life."
RAT: One and the same, my dear Mole, one and the same.
  (Music, sings.)
    Life on the river is gentle;
    Willow trees bow to the sky.
    Problems become elemental, my friend,
    Letting the river flow by.
    See how the flotsam is drifting;
    Thoughts, if you've got some, drift, too.
    Even the flood is up lifting in spring.
    Wait and the world comes to you.
    Life is a river within you.
    Sometimes it's rough for awhile,
    But till the end we continue along.
    What really matters is style.
    Catfish swim side beside minnows,
    Ducklings glide by in a line,
    Birds of all feathers flock innocently,
    Life on the river is fine.
MOLE: That was very good, you know.
RAT: My pleasure. Such a beautiful day for boating. I'm
  surprised there aren't more boats out on the river. Have you
  ever been out?
MOLE: No. Is it nice?
RAT: Nice? It's the only thing. Believe me, my young friend,
  there is nothing, absolutely nothing, as wonderful as simply
  messing about in boats. Simply messing.
MOLE: *(Looks out over Audience with spyglass.)* Is that a boat?
RAT: *(Following his gaze.)* Where?
MOLE: There by the cattails, coming 'round the bend.
RAT: Yes, by juniper, it is! A racing shell by the looks of her.
  My word, isn't that . . . it is! It's Toad!
MOLE: How splendid!
RAT: He's forever up to something new. Then he tires of it
  and starts on something fresh.
MOLE: Such a good fellow, though.
RAT: Yes, but no stability. Especially in boats.
MOLE: I can see him now. Goodness, but he's rowing up a
  storm.
RAT: You may call that rowing, if you're of a generous mind.
  He's missing the water with every other stroke.
MOLE: The splashes look very fine.
RAT: Splashes do not propel a boat at optimal efficiency.
MOLE: He's rolling about like an upturned turtle.
RAT: His oar is stuck. It must be tangled in the weed.
  He's pulling on it. Oh dear, now he's standing up. No,

Toad, no! He's going to . . . Oh!

MOLE: Oh! *(Sound of a loud splash.)*

RAT: Dear me.

MOLE: Oh my, oh my, oh my, oh my.

TOAD: *(ENTERS.)* Ha, HA! Hello you fellows. Kind of you to be here just now. Did you see my ordeal?

RAT: Go for a swim, did you?

TOAD: *(Wrings out his handkerchief.)* I beg your pardon, Rat, but frogs swim. Toads are above all that. No, no, I was speaking of my adventure just now. I was attacked by an alligator.

MOLE: How terrible!

TOAD: Big brute he was. Bit on to my oar, but I wrestled it away from him.

MOLE: You're very brave.

TOAD: Yes, I know.

RAT: My dear Toad, there are no alligators in this river.

TOAD: No?

RAT: No.

TOAD: I didn't have time for a good inspection. Perhaps then it was only a crocodile.

RAT: No.

TOAD: No?

RAT: Perhaps a floating log.

TOAD: With teeth.

MOLE: How extraordinary.

TOAD: Yes, well, an adventure is what you make of it.

RAT: Really, Toad, don't you think it's about time you gave up this careless boating of yours before you have an accident?

TOAD: As a matter of fact, I do.

RAT: You do?

TOAD: I'm through with it, as of today. Made up my mind this very morning.

RAT: Take his pulse, Mole. That splash must have wetted his brain. Do you feel all right, Toad?

TOAD: Never better. Ha, HA! I've discovered the real thing, the only genuine occupation for a lifetime. I propose to devote the remainder of mine to it, and can only regret the wasted years that lie behind me, squandered in trivialities.

MOLE: What is it?

TOAD: The open road!

MOLE: That sounds wonderful!

TOAD: Wonderful? It is magnificent! Think of it, Mole. The open road, the dusty highway, over hill and under dale. Camps, villages, towns, cities! Here today, up and off to somewhere else tomorrow! The whole world before you, and a horizon that's always changing! And I want you both to come with me. You, Mole, and you, too, Rat. Yes! Adventure enough for all of us. Now wait right here. Don't go away, I'll be right back. I've got it parked just upstream. *(TOAD EXITS.)*

RAT: It? It?

MOLE: Oh, the road, the open road, the glorious, fabulous open road! Ratty, what's a road?

RAT: A road is very much like a river, without the advantages of moving, although it goes places and is dry and dusty and is not at all peaceful or refreshing.

MOLE: Can you wash in it?

RAT: I would advise heartily against it.

MOLE: Then I can't think how it is very like a river at all.

BADGER: *(ENTERS, carrying a cane.)* Hello, there.

RAT: Why, it's none other than Badger.

MOLE: How do you do, Mr. Badger, sir.

BADGER: Have you seen hide or scale of Toad hereabouts?

RAT: Why, yes, as a matter of fact . . .

BADGER: He's been at it again, up and down the river causing chaos and disrupting the peace like a tidal wave of irresponsibility. Only this time he's gone too far. I've been approached by a spokesman of the Duck Committee. They're quacking mad, I can tell you. This time they really have their down up. This morning Toad blithely rowed headlong into a gaggle of feeding ducks with their tails in the air, scattering them like ten-pins at a tournament.

RAT: I think from now on the ducks may paddle at ease.

BADGER: How's that?

MOLE: Toad's given up the river.

BADGER: If that's the case then he's up to even greater no good. Toad doesn't give things up. They give out on him.

RAT: Quite so. He's taken up the open road.

MOLE: He told us not to move. He's gone upstream to get it.

BADGER: It? What's it?

TOAD: *(ENTERS with a colorful gypsy wagon. Sound: horse's whinny and hoofbeats. The horse may be played by an actor or actors in a horse suit.)* Here it is! Ha, HA!

RAT: It's a gypsy wagon!

MOLE: Oh, it's beautiful. May I touch it?

TOAD: Touch it? You must ride it! *(Music: "The Open Road" Sings:)*

> Hurry up, pack the basket,
> Have no fear, or else mask it.
> If we lose our way we'll ask it, on the open road.

No more hesitating now adventure is waiting,
Far beyond anticipating by an ordinary toad.

Bring some tea and a crumpet, blow the horn,
Sound the trumpet.
If we see a fence we'll jump it on the open road.

MOLE: May I go, Ratty, please?

RAT: You are free to do as you like, Mole. You needn't have my permission.

MOLE: Yes, but I want it.

TOAD: Now, Ratty, don't begin talking in that stiff and sniffy sort of way, because you know you've got to come, too. I can't possibly manage without you, so please consider it settled and don't argue. It's the one thing I can't stand. I want to show you the world! I'm going to make an animal of you, my boy!

RAT: Thank you but I quite prefer the river.

MOLE: Oh, well, then I suppose I won't go either.

TOAD: What's the matter with you two? Adventure beckons! Excitement with every turn of the wheel, 'round every turn in the road!

RAT: You really want to go, don't you, Mole?

MOLE: Oh, yes, more than lunch.

RAT: Well, I imagine a turn around the boulevard won't hurt anyone.

MOLE: Oh, rapture!

TOAD: That's the spirit! Up you go. Your turn, Badger. Don't be a stick-in-the-mud. *(THEY get into wagon.)*

BADGER: Better than to sink into it. But I shall be here to pull you out. You know I don't approve of your shenanigans, Toad. When I told your father I would look after you, little did I realize you would become a full-time headache as well as a hazard to fish and fowl. Along with Toad Hall you inherited a position of responsibility. You must conduct your-self in a manner befitting your wealth and social stature. But why do I lecture you? You never listen.

TOAD: What did you say, Badger?

BADGER: Rat, I appeal to you. Don't encourage him.

RAT: Just a harmless ride.

TOAD: Right, then. We're off! Hold on to your tails. *(Music.)*

MOLE: *(Sings.)*
Oh my gosh, oh my golly!

RAT: *(Sings.)*
I admit it's rather jolly.

BADGER: *(Sings.)*
    I consider it a folly on the open road.
    Rat, you know it's silly,
    'Round in circles willy-nilly.
RAT: *(Sings.)*
    But until he has his fill he won't be willing to unload.
TOAD: *(Sings.)*
    Let the rabbits be wary, it's my habit not to tarry.
    Only speed is necessary on the open road.
    (The sound of a motor is heard distantly.)
MOLE: *(Sings.)*
    Listen up, what's that humming? *(MOLE hums.)*
RAT: *(Sings.)*
    No, it sounds more like drumming. *(RAT drums.)*
TOAD: *(Sings.)*
    Rat, I think there's something coming down the open road.
RAT: *(Sings.)*
    Toad, please mind the steering.
    Now the wagon is veering and that awful thing is nearing,
    Oh, it's going to explode!
(The sound of a motor car grows loud on one side of the stage and zooms by, upsetting the wagon and its occupants who scatter on the ground. If a horse is used, he rears and runs off.)
RAT: *(Picking himself up, dusting himself off.)* You villains! You scoundrels, you highwaymen, you . . . you . . . . road-hogs!
MOLE: Goodness, all the dust! Are you all right, Ratty?
RAT: Apart from my dignity and a few bruises, yes. Where's Toad?
MOLE: Over there.
RAT: I say, Toad, are you injured? Toad?
MOLE: Toady?
TOAD: Putt-putt.
RAT: What did he say?
MOLE: I think he said, "putt-putt". Mean anything to you?
RAT: It means we have a problem on our hands, and it isn't warts.
TOAD: Putt-putt. Putt-putt! B-r-r-r-o-o-o-om!
RAT: Come on, Toad, snap out of it! Mole, get some water.
TOAD: Glorious, stirring sight! The poetry of motion! The real way to travel. The ONLY way to travel! Villages skipped, towns and cities jumped, always somebody else's horizon! Oh, bliss. Oh, putt-putt!
MOLE: What is he raving about?

RAT: What does he always rave about? Himself, of course.

BADGER: *(Coming up.)* Well, at least I won't have to hear from the Duck Committee about this incident.

MOLE: Did you see it, Mr. Badger, sir? All that noise and dust and commotion?

BADGER: All that noise and dust and commotion is called a motor-car.

TOAD: Motor-car!

BADGER: Nasty, smelly human things.

TOAD: Motor-car! I must have one. I must have one now, this very moment. I shall be utterly miserable until I have that magic wheel in my hands, the wheel of fortune! I must have a motor-car! *(TOAD dashes OFF.)*

BADGER: We must save him.

RAT: Oh, bother Toad! I've done with him. Him and his carts and cars. It isn't natural. Animals were never meant to ride in motor-cars. The Good Lord knows the only decent way to travel is in a boat.

BADGER: I am glad to hear your senses restored to you. None-theless, we must rescue him from his folly.

RAT: Give me one good reason.

BADGER: I shall give you THE reason, which is none other than the very foundation of society itself, the guiding principle of our civilization, without which we animals would become like humans! Duty! *(THEY have stepped forward and the curtain closes behind them.)*

RAT: Duty.

BADGER: Yes, duty to our fellow animals. Toad may hurt him-self, or even if he doesn't, pity the poor, frightened animals run over by his motorized onslaught. Rat, where is your honor, your nobility, your animality?

RAT: Forgive me, Badger. We'll rescue the poor, unhappy animal! We'll convert him! He'll be the most converted Toad that ever was before we're done.

MOLE: Hooray!

RAT: Onward! For Toad and country! *(THEY EXIT. Curtain.)*

Scene Three
The Open Road

The curtain opens. A shiny new motor-car is parked on one side of the stage, pointed OFF. TOAD ENTERS opposite dressed in a motorists' duster, cap with goggles. As he *CROSSES* he sings a capella to the tune of "The Open Road".

TOAD: *(Sings.)* Now the future looks fairer,
   And unless I've made an error, Toad will prove to be a

9

terror of the o- . . . *(Gasps.)*
What do I behold before my bulging eyes but the beautiful body of a motor-car! In the flesh! *(He looks furtively about, then approaches the car.)* There can't be any harm in my only just LOOKING at it. What a work of art! The grace, the clean-swept lines, the power. And all to one lofty purpose: speed! Surely there can't be any harm in my only just TOUCHING it. *(He does.)* Ooh! Nature has never known its like. And surely there can't be any harm in my only just SITTING in it. *(He does.)* There, see? No harm done. I wonder what this doo-hickey is for. Well, surely there can't be any harm in my only just . . . *(Sound of the motor starting.)* Ha, HA! *(The car and TOAD leap forward and OFF STAGE. [NOTE: If a fixed set piece is being used as the motor-car, TOAD can mime its sudden acceleration, then throw his hands over his face to hide from the impending crash, followed by a sudden blackout to cover his EXIT.] Sound: Resounding crash followed by a police whistle. RAT, MOLE and BADGER ENTER from the same direction that TOAD did previously.)*

RAT: He can't be very far.

MOLE: Do you suppose he's lost?

BADGER: If he is he wouldn't know it.

RAT: Halt!

MOLE: What is it?

RAT: Shh! Listen.

MOLE: It's a LITTLE scary.

RAT: We've come to the edge of the Wild Wood. We dare venture no further. Toad is on his own.

BADGER: *(Pointing OFF STAGE where the motor-car went.)* What's that?

RAT: Wreckage, it appears. Some sort of mild catastrophe. Wait here . . . I'll go see. *(He returns with a steering wheel and TOAD'S goggles.)*

MOLE: It's Toad!

RAT: It was Toad.

MOLE: He's not . . .

RAT: He's gone.

MOLE: Oh, no!!!

RAT: Calm yourself, Mole. I meant he's vanished. Gone with the wind.

BADGER: Then good riddance, I say, and we're all the better off for it.

MOLE: Oh, no, Mr. Badger.

BADGER: Terrorizing the countryside like that! It's a wonder he didn't squash a chipmunk or pulverize a caterpillar.
MOLE: Where do you suppose he's gone to, then?
RAT: On the other side is the Wide World.
BADGER: Off to be a human. Well, let him, then, if he can't behave like an animal. We'll have no more to do with him. Since he has renounced us . . .
MOLE: He only wanted some fun.
BADGER: . . . we will renounce him. Toad is no longer an animal.
RAT: Oh, I think that's a bit severe.
BADGER: Henceforth, the name of Toad is banished from polite conversation along the riverbank. Let no animal mention that name again!
MOLE: Does that mean we can't like Toad anymore?
BADGER: Who?
MOLE: Toad.
RAT: Mole, you're not supposed to mention that name.
MOLE: What name?
RAT: Toad. Oh, sorry.
BADGER: Hmph! Come along. Our business here is finished. *(He EXITS.)*
RAT: He's in quite a huff.
MOLE: Will he never forgive Toa- , er . . . him, you know?
RAT: Don't worry. We'll have a talk with Badger. He'll come 'round.
MOLE: *(Looking after TOAD.)* I imagine HE'S very lonely, wherever HE is.
RAT: Come along, Mole. You can say a prayer for him tonight, if you like.
MOLE: Good-bye, *(Sniffs.)* friend. *(THEY EXIT.)*

Scene Four
The Court

JUDGE: *(ENTERS to one of the large set pieces which, as he adds the scales of justice, becomes a judge's bench. TOAD ENTERS opposite, wearing an oversized pair of handcuffs. JUDGE pounds his gavel.)* Silence in the Court! Court is now in session, the Honorable Judge Thwackbottom presiding. That's me. Ladies and gentlemen of the jury, we are convened to hear the case of The People versus Toad. Will the defendant please stand? *(Indicating TOAD.)* That's you. You're the defendant. Stand up.
TOAD: I am standing.

JUDGE: State your full name.
TOAD: Toad.
JUDGE: Your FULL name.
TOAD: The Great and Glorious Toad.
JUDGE: The defendant will now take the stand. Sit down! You are justly accused of stealing a motor-car and wrecking it. How do you plead?
TOAD: I object!
JUDGE: Call me Your Honor.
TOAD: My Honor, I object.
JUDGE: Not YOUR Honor, your HONOR.
TOAD: Your Honor, My Honor, I object.
JUDGE: You can't object, you're the defendant.
TOAD: I demand a fair trial.
JUDGE: This is a fair trial. The unfair part comes later.
TOAD: I wish to be tried by a jury of my peers, a jury of animals. *(Indicating Audience.)* These are all people.
JUDGE: You broke a human law and therefore it is just that you be tried by human law. Besides, you have no choice. It's this or the "slammer". Take it or leave it. Now, do you plead guilty or not guilty?
TOAD: Hungry.
JUDGE: That's not the choice.
TOAD: A menu isn't necessary.
JUDGE: Guilty or not guilty?
TOAD: How about a grasshopper?
JUDGE: Did you take that motor-car?
TOAD: No. On my honor, Your Honor.
JUDGE: You didn't take that motor-car?
TOAD: No, it took me. I just sat in it.
JUDGE: Then you're guilty.
TOAD: Maybe, but couldn't we have lunch first?
JUDGE: Ladies and gentlemen of the jury, you must now decide . . .
TOAD: I object.
JUDGE: Objection overruled.
TOAD: I object to your overruling my objection.
JUDGE: Shut up!
TOAD: Shan't.
JUDGE: You're in contempt.
TOAD: And here I thought I was in court. I demand my right to a proper defense.
JUDGE: Oh, very well, but you're only wasting your time. I've already made up my mind.
TOAD: Ahem. If it please the court . . . *(Music: "The Great And Glorious Toad". Sings.)*

I am the Great and Glorious Toad,
My story is destined for history.
In all the world there never has been one clever as me.

When I was just a silly lad on a lily pad,
I learned to my surprise that life was more
    than following rules and swallowing flies.

JUDGE: *(Sings.)*
No crime in being curious but the jury is not going
    to set you free,
For driving fast and furious and injuriously.

I seldom grant defendants their independence;
They're guilty till proven not.
It's time you started fretting a bit and sweating a lot.

TOAD: *(Sings.)* | JUDGE: *(Sings.)*

I am the Great and Glorious
Toad, my story is destined for
    history.
In all the world there never has
    been one clever as me.

For someone great and
    glorious what a bore he is:
All that he wants is food.
His boasting is uproarious
    and what's more he is rude.

When I was just a silly lad
    on a lily pad
I learned to my surprise
That life was more than following
    rules and swallowing flies.

No crime in being curious
But the jury is not
    going to set you free
For driving fast and furious
    and injuriously.

This is the Great and Glorious
    Toad.   Not sorry is he.

The Glorious,
Euphorious, uproarious,
Mysterious,
Delirious,
Incredible,
Unedible,
Toad.

I've had enough
    retort
My temper has
    run short,
And as a last
    resort,
You're in contempt
    of court.

Leave it to me and you will see
No tearful plea on bended knee.
I will go free, I will go free,

Leave it to me and you will see
A century without a key.
You won't go free, you won't
    go free.

I will go free, go free, go free,	You won't go free, go free, go free,
Go free, go free!	Go free, go free!

JUDGE: That's enough! The defense may rest. The judge has to rest.

TOAD: But I'm not through.

JUDGE: Maybe not, but I'm through with you. *(To Audience.)* The jury will now consider very carefully the evidence against Toad. All the rest you may disregard. That's enough time. What is your verdict? Is Toad guilty? *(Audience responds Ad lib.)* You're all overruled. I'm the judge. *(Alternate response.* You're right.) He's as guilty as the ace of spades. Well, Toad, do you have any last words before I pronounce sentence? *(TOAD razzes the JUDGE.)* Now for the unfair part. First, for the crime of stealing a valuable motor-car, you are sentenced to thirty days in prison. Second, for the outrage of driving recklessly and endangering the public you are sentenced to an additional six months. Third, for the insufferable disrespect you have paid to the dignity of this court, another ninety-nine years. However, the court in its benevolence finds it in my heart to suspend the entire sentence and let you go free, if you promise solemnly to go home and live out your natural life as an ordinary toad, and to give up motor-cars entirely and forever, and to admit before all assembled here you are sorry for how you behaved and you see the folly of it all.

TOAD: Never, never, never, not in ninety-nine hundred years! It wasn't folly at all. It was simply glorious!

JUDGE: You know what you're saying?

TOAD: Yes, the truth. I'm not sorry and I can't lie about it. Animals never lie.

JUDGE: Come along then. I shall take you to prison myself. You have only yourself to blame. *(JUDGE pulls TOAD off by the ear.)*

TOAD: I shall return! They haven't built a jail small enough to hold the Great and Glorious Toad! *(THEY EXIT.)*

Scene Five
Rat's House

RAT: *(ENTERS with a tea kettle. He putters about, dusting the furniture or adjusting his favorite chair in such a way that it is obvious he is at home. A knock is heard OFF STAGE.)* Come in, Mole. You know my door is always open.

14

MOLE: *(ENTERS, dressed in muffler, earmuffs and mittens.)*
Hello, Rat.

RAT: Hello, Mole. You must be half frozen.

MOLE: It is cold. Feels like snow. Winter is once more
upon us, I'm afraid.

RAT: Here, bring a chair to the fire. Why aren't you
hibernating?

MOLE: Can't sleep, thinking of poor old Toa . . . I mean,
things.

RAT: Yes. How about a spot of piping hot tea? I can put
the kettle on.

MOLE: No, thank you.

RAT: Won't take but a minute.

MOLE: No, really.

RAT: Well, it's jolly to see you, although I expect you're not
here for the company.

MOLE: Whenever I try to sleep I hear the wind. Have you
noticed? It's changed. Howling.

RAT: A storm brewing, perhaps.

MOLE: I hear crying, Rat, the shedding of lonesome tears, and
the faraway, unanswered call for help.

RAT: I've heard.

MOLE: It's been months since . . . since the accident. The
ducks have all flown south. The river is sealed with ice.
Ratty, we must find him, you know.

RAT: Who?

MOLE: You know who.

RAT: Alas, I do. And where do you propose to look?

MOLE: Oh, here and there and roundabout. Under leaves, in
trees. The world can't be so large as to keep very long from
us a single toad . . . animal.

RAT: A single-toed animal?

MOLE: Or one with webbed feet.

RAT: See here, my nearsighted friend, the world is a far larger
place than you or I have any business to imagine. There are
great dangers beyond the river, strange creatures and dark
corners where a dozen moles might be swallowed up never to
be heard from again.

MOLE: Still, we must do something.

RAT: Yes, you're right. We must, at least, try. I don't expect
to get much peace around here until he's back again bothering
me. But we shan't go unprepared. Wait a moment. *(RAT
EXITS, returns with a backpack from which he hands a pop-
gun to MOLE.)* Here, can you handle one of these?

MOLE: Oh, yes. *(Takes gun, points it at RAT.)* What does it
do?

RAT: Hold on. Better take this, it's more your size.
(He exchanges the pop-gun for a wooden sword.)
MOLE: *(Swishing the sword about.)* Oh, this is grand!
RAT: Now, we must go about this scientifically, if we hope
to entertain any chance of success.
MOLE: Scientifically?
RAT: Precisely. Once we have looked in a place without
finding him, we must only look thereafter someplace else,
for we shall have proved in the first place that he is not
in the first place and in the second place that he will un-
doubtedly be in the last place we look.
MOLE: Maybe we should start there then.
RAT: Where?
MOLE: In the last place.
RAT: *(Putting on the backpack.)* Come along, Mole.
MOLE: What's in that?
RAT: Enough food for a week. Emergency provisions.
Pickled herring, smoked bacon, blueberry muffins, ginger beer,
just the essentials. You see, I've been prepared for you some
time now.
MOLE: You've certainly not been idle.
RAT: Right then, let's be off. Time and Toad wait for no
animal.
MOLE: Rat, you spoke his name.
RAT: Really, Mole, did you think I'd forgotten? *(THEY EXIT.)*

Scene Six
The Prison

TOAD: *(ENTERS wearily, dragging a large ball and chain which
is shackled to his ankle and upon which he sits. He is wearing a striped prison jersey. He sings a capella to the tune of
"The Great and Glorious Toad".*
I am the Great and Glorious Toad,
My story is come to a bitter end.
Woe is me. This is the end of everything. At least it is the
end of the career of Toad, which is the same thing. Now I
must languish in this dungeon, till animals who were proud to
say they knew me have forgotten the very name of Toad.
Oh, if only my friends were here with me now. Why, Mole
could dig his way out, Ratty could think his way out, Badger
could talk his way out, but I? *(In despair.)* I could croak.
(WASHERWOMAN ENTERS with laundry basket.) Here comes
the Judge. This may be my very last chance to do something
right. I shall drop immediately to my knees before him and
beg for mercy. *(He tries.)* No use. Pride doesn't bend.

WOMAN: Shhh!

TOAD: I shan't shush. *(Arrogantly.)* You can cage me like a bird. You can beat me like a mule, flog me as a frog, starve me, chain me, even tickle me, but you can never silence me. My mouth is my own. I am the Great and Glorious . . .

WOMAN: *(She claps her hand over his mouth.)* Mercy and landsakes, do be quiet! I haven't any time for your silly prattling. The guards are everywhere. Now be good.

TOAD: You can't make me call you My Honor, neither.

WOMAN: I should hope not. My name is Alice.

TOAD: Alice? Alice is no proper name for a judge.

WOMAN: You'll be insulting me soon. I do the washing for the prison, a profession far more honorable than that which sent you here.

TOAD: My apologies. You must understand, it's difficult to tell you humans apart.

WOMAN: Maybe for you. But you should please understand that we do not act alike at all. *(Sound OFFSTAGE.)* Footsteps! It's the guard on his rounds. Be natural. *(Sound disappears.)* He's gone.

TOAD: You humans do act most peculiarly.

WOMAN: Shh! I could lose my job, if I was caught.

TOAD: Talking to a toad? Seems a bit unfair.

WOMAN: No, no, no! WILL you listen? I'm here to rescue you, you silly Toad.

TOAD: Rescue? Me? A mere washerwoman? How do I know this isn't a trap?

WOMAN: The Saints preserve me from violence to a lower form of life! Very well. You see, I'm very fond of wee little animals, especially toads. When I was but a girl in knee-socks, I kept a toad as a pet.

TOAD: Horrors!

WOMAN: Oh, but I was very kind to him. We would play a game: I was a princess and he was a prince turned into a toad by an evil spell which I could break by kissing him. Well, you see what happened. I grew up and learned it wasn't right to keep animals in cages of any sort. Look, I've borrowed the jailer's key. We must hurry before it's missed. *(She CROSSES toward TOAD who reacts as if he were being threatened.)*

TOAD: You can't kiss me!

WOMAN: *(Unlocks the chain which slips off TOAD'S ankle.)* There.

TOAD: *(Gasps.)* I'm . . . free. FREE! Ha-HA!

WOMAN: Shush, or we'll both be locked up!

TOAD: *(Skipping about.)* Free, free, free, free . . .

WOMAN: Yes, yes, mercy and landsakes, but for how long?

TOAD: (Stops.) Huh?

WOMAN: Do you expect to skip on past the gatekeeper singing, "free, free, free"?

TOAD: I hadn't thought about that.

WOMAN: That is your chief trouble; you don't think. And you talk too much, which is your chief fault. The combination is most irritating.

TOAD: (Suddenly thinks.) The guard!

WOMAN: Oh! Where, where?

TOAD: What if I meet up with the guard?

WOMAN: (Clutching her chest.) If I don't get you out of here soon, you'll be the death of me. I have a plan. In my basket is one of my dresses and a bonnet. Disguise yourself in these and you may walk out of this dungeon with head held high as an official washerwoman.

TOAD: I'll do no such thing! That would be deceitful, and not at all fitting for a toad of my stature.

WOMAN: Oh, it will fit all right. We're very alike in many respects, particularly about the figure.

TOAD: We're not. I have a very elegant figure.

WOMAN: Have it your own way, you horrid, proud, ungrateful animal. Here I'm sorry for you and trying to help you. You may as well lock yourself up again this moment and save the guards the trouble.

TOAD: Look here, you surely wouldn't have Mr. Toad of Toad Hall going about the country disguised as a washerwoman.

WOMAN: I suppose you want to go tripping off in a carriage drawn by eight white mice.

TOAD: Very well. You leave me no choice. But I hope the history books, when they're written, neglect to mention the particular and humiliating manner of my daring escape. (The prison jersey is removed. TOAD holds out his arms and the WOMAN dresses him in a long dress, bonnet and shawl while TOAD grimaces.)

WOMAN: You're the very image of me. Only I'm sure you never looked half so respectable in all your life. Now, good-bye Toad, and good luck.

TOAD: About the dress . . .

WOMAN: Keep it, I have others. Go!

TOAD: It's the color. Do you have something in an aquamarine?

WOMAN: (Shoves him OFF.) Be off with you. And don't look back. (She blows him a kiss.) He didn't even say thank-you. Just like a toad. (Sound of police whistles and shouting from OFFSTAGE.) Oh! Run, Toad, run! (She takes up her basket, runs OFF opposite.) Toad!? What toad? I don't know any toad.

Scene Seven
The Wild Wood

Lights dim. Creepy sounds of a scary place; roars, shrieks and
howls, made by actors backstage. This scene may be played
in front of the curtain. RAT is heard calling before he ENTERS.

RAT: Toad! I say, Toad! *(ENTERS, followed at some dis-
tance by a flagging MOLE.)* Toad? *(Looks around.)* Mole!
Mole, we can't let ourselves become separated out here in the
Wild Wood or it might prove fatal. You must try to keep up.

MOLE: Couldn't you try instead to keep down?

RAT: Really, with that attitude we shall never get anywhere.

MOLE: I'm sorry, but I'm dreadfully tired. Couldn't we just
stop and rest? Perhaps Toad will come by.

RAT: It's not in the schedule. But . . . I suppose we could
take an early dinner.

MOLE: Oh, thank you, Rat.

RAT: Only we must make up for it afterwards. We've been
lucky so far. The snow has held off, but for how much longer
I've no idea.

MOLE: Then we had better eat. *(MOLE plops down.)*

RAT: Not here, for goodness' sake, in the open with who knows
what manner of strangeness all about. Where is your sense?

MOLE: It must have run out along with my breath.

RAT: We'll need some shelter, some sort of protection from the
elements. Over here. Give a hand, will you? We can fashion
a rough but quite suitable nest from these fallen branches.

MOLE: It's cozy. Not much like home. Although home is not
much.

RAT: We had better huddle together to preserve warmth.

MOLE: What's for dinner?

RAT: *(Looking in his backpack.)* Sausage and sweetbreads.

MOLE: Any port in a storm.

RAT: We can pretend we're picnicking along the river in July.
The sun is warm. There, can you hear the meadowlark?

MOLE: *(Listening.)* No.

RAT: It's only pretend.

MOLE: I'm sorry, Ratty, but I find it difficult to pretend just
now, under the circumstances.

RAT: Look here, Mole, are you sorry we came?

MOLE: No, no, no. But, forgive me, Rat, I can't forget where
I might have been just now, snug in my favorite chair in front
of the fire, warming my paws on a mug of hot punch.

RAT: Home.

MOLE: Do we ever know just where it is, except when we're
  not there?

RAT: No, indeed. *(Music.)*

MOLE: *(Sings: "Home".)*

> Home, to a mole, is much more than a hole,
> So much more than a bore in the ground.
> Home, to a mole, is a nest where the soul
> Takes a rest in the best digs around.
> Far from the hassle of life in full swing,
> Home is the castle where mole is the king.
> Some need a dome made of glass, gilt and chrome;
> As for me, let me be in my mound underground
> Far below, for there's no place like home.

RAT: *(Sings.)*

> Home, to a rat, is the place where it's at:
> My own space when the race has been run.
> Home, to a rat, is a hook for my hat;
> Just a nook where the cooking is done.
> Far from the hassle of life in full swing,
> Home is the castle where rat is the king.

BOTH: *(Sing.)*

> Some need a dome made of glass, gilt and chrome;
> As for me, let me be in my mound underground
> Far below, for there's no place like home.

RAT: Time to shove off. As miserable as we are, think how
  much worse off Toad is with neither you nor I nor anyone
  for company. Stay close, Mole. I'm afraid the Wood gets
  darker up ahead. *(THEY EXIT.)*

Scene Eight
The Railway

ENGINEER ENTERS with an oil can and tends to the locomotive.
As he fusses and polishes, TOAD ENTERS hurriedly, still garbed in
dress and bonnet.

TOAD: Aha! This is a piece of luck. Here I have run upon
  the world's largest motorcar. And look what improvements have
  been made since my imprisonment. Now it runs on a road of
  steel rails. I won't have the bother of steering it. *(He starts
  to sneak aboard.)*

ENGINEER: Hello, woman. What brings you out on a night
  such as this?

TOAD: *(Surprised in the act.)* Who are you?

20

ENGINEER: McDougal's the name and proud of it, like me
father before me. Now state your business.
TOAD: *(Adopting a falsetto voice.)* Your pardon, sir. Perhaps
you could give me a ride on your big, fine, powerful
motorcar.
ENGINEER: Motorcar, is it! I'll take that for a jest. This
here is a railroad engine. Her name is Betsy, and she's the
finest machine ever to breathe steam and ride the rails of the
Hither, Thither and Yon Railroad Company. She's me pride
and joy, and if you'll be wanting to ride her, you can march
down to the station and buy a ticket.
TOAD: Your pardon again. Being old, my eyes do not see so
well anymore, and now, what with the tears welling up . . .
(He takes out his handkerchief, wipes his eyes, blows his nose.)
ENGINEER: Here now, what's the trouble?
TOAD: Oh, sir! I am a poor unhappy washerwoman, and I've
lost my purse, and can't pay for a ticket, and I must get
home tonight, and whatever I am to do, I don't know. Oh,
dear, oh dear.
ENGINEER: That's a bad business, indeed. Lost your money,
and can't get home, and got some kids waiting for you, I dare
say.
TOAD: Oh, any number of them. *(He sobs.)*
ENGINEER: Well, I'll tell you what I'll do. You're a washerwoman to your trade says you. Very well, that's that. And
I'm the engineer on this here train and there's no denying it's
terribly dirty work. Now, if you'll wash a few shirts for me
when you get home, and send 'em along, I'll give you a ride
on my engine. It's against the Company's regulations, but
just between you and me, who's to know, eh?
TOAD: Oh, sir, you are too kind. *(Dropping into his normal
voice.)* Could we hurry?
ENGINEER: All aboard then. Mind your step. *(THEY climb
onto the locomotive.)* Here we go! *(He pulls on a cord to
blow the whistle. Music: "The Railroad Track".)*
TOAD: Now this is the life!
ENGINEER: It does all right by me.
TOAD: Ha-HA! And no trees to smash into. *(Sings.)*
Let her rip, there's no stopping; though my eyes and ears
are popping.
What the heck! It sure beats hopping,
Down the railroad track.

Motor cars are boring, next to this . . . this is soaring.
Like a comet we are roaring, smoke is pouring from the
stack.

See the cows, how they cower.
Oh, what joy! Oh, what power,
Going twenty miles an hour down the railroad track!

ENGINEER: *(Looks back. The music continues underneath.)*
Here now, what's up? It's very strange. We're the last train
running in this direction tonight, yet I could swear I heard
another following us.

TOAD: What!?

ENGINEER: I can see it clearly now. We're being chased!

TOAD: *(Desperately grabbing a lever or control on the locomotive.)* Can't we go any faster?

ENGINEER: Let go of that! Do you want to wreck us?
(Forces TOAD to let go of the lever.)

TOAD: Save me, only save me and I will confess. I am Toad,
the well-known and popular Mr. Toad of Toad Hall who has
just escaped from prison.

ENGINEER: Now, tell the truth! What were you put in prison
for?

TOAD: It was nothing very much. I only borrowed a motorcar
and along the way I happened to smash it up a bit.

ENGINEER: By rights I ought to turn you in. But I don't
hold with motorcars for one thing; and I don't hold with being
chased about when I'm on my own engine, for another. *(Sings.)*
You're a toad with no virtue
But if those men want to hurt you
Then McDougal won't desert you on the railroad track.
Though your time may seem up
If the two of us will team up
We can get a head of steam up that will leave them way,
way, back.
(Spoken.) Come on, Betsy! *(Sings.)*
Ring the bell, blow the whistle!
Let our foes know that this'll be like trying to chase a
missle,
Down the railroad track!
(Spoken.) I'm afraid it's no good, Toad. They're gaining on us.

TOAD: It's chains and bread and water and misery once more for
poor, unhappy, innocent Toad.

ENGINEER: Wait! Up ahead!

TOAD: I can't see anything. It's very dark up ahead.

ENGINEER: Exactly! We're coming to a tunnel. Get ready.
As soon as we're through it, I'll put on the brakes as hard as
I can. Then you jump and hide in the wood.

TOAD: Jump?

ENGINEER: Hop then; you're a toad.

TOAD: While we're *(Swallows hard.)* moving?

ENGINEER: No time to think about it. Here comes the tunnel! *(Lights go out, sounds of a train, the lights come on. TOAD is cowering behind the ENGINEER.)* Come on, jump!

TOAD: Maybe prison isn't so bad . . .

ENGINEER: Jump!!! *(He shoves TOAD off. TOAD scrambles to his feet and scampers OFF. ENGINEER rides the locomotive OFF STAGE as the music fades out. If a fixed set piece is being used as the locomotive, the lights should go out to cover the ENGINEER'S EXIT.)*

Scene Nine
The Wild Wood

Even creepier sounds of an even scarier place. RAT and MOLE ENTER.

MOLE: *(Hanging timidly onto the coat-tails of RAT.)* Ratty, I'm frightened.

RAT: There, there. It can't go on forever.

MOLE: I feel there are a hundred pairs of eyes watching . . . watching, but every time I turn, they vanish. There! *(Turns abruptly, scaring RAT.)*

RAT: What . . . ! Please don't do that any more, Mole.

MOLE: Sorry.

RAT: We must not panic, we must stay calm, we must . . . oh, heavens!

MOLE: *(Jumps.)* What, what?

RAT: *(Looking down on the ground.)* A footprint. Well, nothing to be alarmed about. *(Alarmed.)* And another! Someone, or something, is up ahead.

MOLE: Ohhhhhh!

RAT: Now, don't fret. It isn't a very large footprint.

MOLE: Still, it might be a horribly big monster with small feet.

RAT: Highly unlikely. Forward, Mole. What's up ahead can't be any worse than what's behind.

MOLE: *(Following in RAT'S footsteps, MOLE notices something.)* Ratty?

RAT: What now?

MOLE: They're your footprints.

RAT: Don't be silly, Mole. How can I be up ahead when I'm right here? *(He tries fitting his foot to the footprint in front of him.)* You're right! It fits. Then that means . . . we've been travelling in circles.

MOLE: I thought I recognized the unknown hereabouts.

RAT: Ashamed as I am to admit it, I'm quite lost.

MOLE: No, you're not. You're right here.

RAT: Yes, but where is here? And worse, how can we possibly get THERE?

MOLE: Which there is that?

RAT: Out of here.

MOLE: Perhaps we could retrace our footprints . . . oh, I see what you mean!

RAT: I've let you down.

MOLE: No, no, not at all. At least we have proved to our satisfaction that Toad isn't in this terrible place.

RAT: Forgive me, Moley, I was forgetting myself for an instant. We shall try a new direction. Stiff upper whiskers! *(RAT marches on.)*

MOLE: *(His pant-cuff is caught on a branch.)* Just a moment, I seem to be caught on a . . . *(He pulls free, tumbling to the ground. Getting up, he has lost his bearings and heads off in another direction.)* Wait for me, Rat. Ratty?

RAT: Stay close, Mole. Mole? *(THEY creep around in the gloom, looking for each other, missing one another, and finally run into each other. Frightened, they run apart until they realize whom they have seen.)*

MOLE: *(Running to RAT, embracing him.)* If it's all the same, dear Ratty, I would still rather be lost with you than without you.

RAT: Hold my hand, Mole. We shall see this through together.

MOLE: I'm glad Toad wasn't here to see me so frightened.

RAT: If it is any small comfort to you, I am frightened, too.

MOLE: Are there lions in the Wild Wood, Ratty?

RAT: Gracious, no. What ever gave you that idea?

MOLE: I thought I heard a growl. Maybe it was my stomach.

RAT: There are no lions in these parts. Quite impossible. Probably just a bear.

MOLE: Do bears like mole meat?

RAT: I shouldn't think so. No, they prefer rat, when they can get it. *(Realizing what he has said.)* Ohhh!

MOLE: Ohhh! *(THEY hug each other, closing their eyes tightly against their fear. Music: "The Piper At The Gates Of Dawn". The sound of a flute is heard floating through the dark.)*

RAT: Soft! Listen! No, it's gone.

MOLE: What?

RAT: So beautiful and strange and new I almost wish now I had never heard it. For an instant so fleeting it roused a longing that is painful, but sweet.

MOLE: Are you running a fever, Rat? *(Music: the flute is heard again.)*

RAT: There! Again! Surely you must hear it, too. *(MOLE shakes his head. RAT starts to follow the music.)*
MOLE: Ratty, don't leave me.
RAT: Music, Mole. Oh, Mole, the beauty of it! Such music I never dreamed of, and the call in it is stronger than all my fears.
MOLE: *(Craning to hear.)* I can't hear it, Ratty. I can't hear anything but the wind.
RAT: It is the wind, Mole. In the willows. I can hear the leaves singing along and the rushing of the river. I hear its song: *(Music comes up, he sings:)*
　　Come to me.
MOLE: Ratty, come back.
RAT: Home, Mole. We're almost home.
MOLE: I can't bear being alone. I'm trying, Ratty, but I can't hear.
RAT: *(Music again, he sings.)*
　　Come to me.
　　(Spoken.) Surely now you must hear it. Ah.
MOLE: *(Hearing it.)* Oh.
RAT: It beckons. We must not resist.
MOLE: But is it safe?
RAT: No, Mole. Not safe. But secure. Put your hand in mine. *(Music. BOTH sing.)*
　　Come animals homeless with no one to guide you;
　　I am beside you; trust to me.
　　There's nothing so hopeless that you can't achieve it,
　　If you will leave it just to me.
MOLE: I'm not afraid anymore.
RAT: Nor I, dear friend. *(The lights begin fading up to bright. RAT and MOLE sing.)*
　　As dawn finds tomorrow in the night
　　Now gone is your sorrow with the light.
MOLE: *(Blinks as if awakened.)* The sun! Oh, Ratty, the sun. It is day.
BADGER: *(ENTERS.)* Heavens be praised, I have found you at long last!
RAT, MOLE: Badger! *(THEY run to him.)*
BADGER: It is a miracle. Here I have searched and searched, and last night when the deepest gloom of despair had finally pierced my resolve, pointing my steps homeward, what did I hear but the most beautiful, unearthly music which I could not refrain from following to this very spot where lo, I find my two dear animals shivering in the dew-damp of morning.
RAT: You heard it, too?
BADGER: Yes, like piping, a flute, or . . . well, now I can't be

too sure. Maybe it was something else, a dove, perhaps, or
the wind. I don't seem to recall. Then I heard your singing,
and your voices guided me the rest of the way.

RAT: Singing? Us?

BADGER: Yes. Whatever possessed you to sing so bravely in
the dark, and in the very depths of the Wild Wood? Well, no
matter. I have found you both, eh? Safe, and that is all that
matters. Come, it is time we started for home.

MOLE: But what about . . .

BADGER: Toad? Yes, I have forgiven him. For bad or worse,
things are not in order without Toad to disrupt them. But first
things first. A steamy bath, a cup of broth, and then we'll
start anew. All of us. *(THEY EXIT.)*

Scene Ten
The Campfire

The THIEF ENTERS, a bunch of animal pelts slung over his
shoulder. He sets down a large pot as if on a campfire, and
begins to stir and taste the broth. TOAD ENTERS cockily, still
garbed in the dress and bonnet. He smells the food which draws
him to the fire where he casually warms his hands. The THIEF
ignores him.

TOAD: A beautiful day for eating, wouldn't you say? Myself,
I prefer breakfast this hour of the morning, but after as many
adventures as I have had, I am not overly particular. Have you
been cooking?

THIEF: *(Grunts.)* Poaching.

TOAD: I generally favor my eggs coddled, and served with toast
and marmalade.

THIEF: Poaching animals. *(He waves the pelts.)*

TOAD: Sir, I am aghast!

THIEF: Be on your way, old maid. Why should I waste
perfectly good food on an old hag of a washerwoman.

TOAD: Old hag!

THIEF: Even your skin has turned green with mold.

TOAD: Washerwoman, indeed! Do not be misled by these
garments, for you, sir, are laboring under the falsest of im-
pressions. *(TOAD strips away his disguise and sings to the
tune of the "Great and Glorious Toad".)*
  I am the Great and Glorious Toad,
  Victorious over my enemies,
  A sudden breeze from nowhere
  I'm free to go where I please . . .

THIEF: Go away, frog. Frog skins aren't worth the cost of a bullet.

TOAD: Frog! You insult me, sir. *(He marches away indignantly, but the smell of food brings him back.)* Perhaps I was a trifle hasty. People do make mistakes. And frogs are not such bad sorts, for slimy fellows. Really, I could make do with a couple of scraps, properly seasoned, and then I'd be hopping off never to bother you again. Of course, I'd gladly pay, but I'm currently out of currency. I could send you a check. I'm very rich, you know, and many are the animals in this forest who would vouch for the great and generous Mr. Toad of Toad Hall.

THIEF: What's that, you say? Rich?

TOAD: Fabulously. Beyond my wildest dreams.

THIEF: In that case, help yourself.

TOAD: Sir, you are too kind. *(THIEF throws a loop of rope around TOAD, tightens it.)* What's going on? Who are you?

THIEF: Allow me to introduce myself. I am Robespierre. I have, in my short but flamboyant career, been thief, brigand, blackguard, cutthroat. My union card. *(He takes out a card printed with "Thief" and displays it.)* I am not above anything vile, despicable, disreputable or plain mean, including the robbery of toads. I see you are impressed. Now, lead on. *(He draws his sword and pokes TOAD.)*

TOAD: Shan't.

THIEF: Oh, shan't you? I'm told frog legs sell for a goodly price at market.

TOAD: I am a Toad!

THIEF: Yes, but I don't seem to know that, do I? *(TOAD hops OFF, followed by the THIEF. A moment later MOLE leads BADGER and RAT on from the opposite direction.)*

MOLE: You see, I was right. I told you I smelled a fire, and food.

BADGER: *(Checking the campfire.)* There were humans here, not friends. Let us keep on our way.

MOLE: *(Sniffing.)* Wait! I smell something amphibious, like Toad.

BADGER: Impossible!

RAT: Come along, Mole. You must have caught a chill in your nose.

BADGER: We've no time for a wild goose chase.

MOLE: It isn't a goose, it's a Toad. I'm sure of it.

BADGER: And it's a human, I tell you.

RAT: Whoever it was, they seem to have gone.

MOLE: Look, a button! *(He bends over, picks up button, holds it up.)* It's Toad's. I'm certain.

BADGER: Let me see that. *(Takes button.)* Yes, it has the Toad Family Crest.

RAT: I recognize it. It's from his vest. Then where . . .
BADGER: (Pointing at the pot.) You don't suppose . . .
MOLE: Oh, no! It's horrible.
RAT: Toad stew.
BADGER: How hungry can a human be?
MOLE: (Crying.) We're too late. It's all my fault.
RAT: I should have listened to you. It's all my fault.
BADGER: No, the blame is mine. I shouldn't have been so
    stern and harsh with him. He wasn't really such a bad fellow,
    for a toad.
ALL: Poor Toad!
BADGER: Let us return to the riverbank, and tell all his friends
    our tidings of grief.
MOLE: Home won't be the same.
RAT: Farewell, Toad. (They EXIT as if in a funeral procession,
    BADGER leading, RAT and MOLE carrying the pot like pall-
    bearers.)

Scene Eleven
Toad Hall

TOAD hops on, still tied with rope, followed by the THIEF, who
is hunched over.

THIEF: When do we get to this Toad Hall of yours? I'm used
    to stooping low, but I warn you, I will not crawl. (He notices
    he can stand up now and does. He sits TOAD down.)
TOAD: Why, sir, this IS Toad Hall. The Grand Foyer, in fact.
THIEF: It's cold and dank.
TOAD: All the comforts of home. I have even installed central
    dampness.
THIEF: Enough of this nonsense. The sooner I get out of here,
    the better. Now, where is this fabulous wealth of yours?
TOAD: In there. (He nods toward OFFSTAGE.)
THIEF: I'll deal with you afterwards, frog. (He EXITS.)
TOAD: (Sings, to the tune of "Home".)
    Home, to a toad,
    Is a lonely abode.
THIEF: (Reappearing.) There is nothing in there but jars and
    jars of flies!
TOAD: My private stock. Some very good years there. I told
    you I was rich.
THIEF: Look, frog, if I do not find money and lots of it very
    soon, I shall become very angry, and when I become very
    angry there is only one thing that will make me happy again,
    and that thing is to kill somebody, even if that somebody
    happens to be an ugly toad with an overly-inflated ego.
    (He EXITS.)

28

TOAD: Money? *(He feels his throat.)* I wonder if he meant me.
(Looks around.) There's no one else here. Oh, me, oh, my.
Ashamed as I am to admit it, I am in dire need of . . .
(Shouts.) HELP! *(Listens.)* What's that? *(Sings.)*
　　Can you hear what I hear?
　　The tweet and the twitter of sparrows and swallows.
(Spoken, to Audience.) Oh, my friends, little animals of the
forest, help me. Send word to Badger, Mole and Rat. Whistle,
chirp, croak! *(He whistles.)* That's it, that's it. If you can
whistle you can help me. *(THIEF returns.)* Oh, he's coming
back . . . shhh!

THIEF: What is all the commotion out here? I can hardly hear
myself ransack. If I don't get my hands on money soon, I'll be
itching to get my hands on you. *(He EXITS.)*

TOAD: Again! *(He whistles.)* Fly, hop, run with my message of
distress. Find Badger and Mole and Rat. Tell them to hurry.
*(He whistles more. BADGER, MOLE and RAT ENTER through
Audience. THEY hear TOAD and Audience members whistling
and speak with various members of the Audience.)*

BADGER: Listen!

MOLE: Toad! He's alive!

RAT: He's a captive in Toad Hall. We must save him.

MOLE: *(To Audience.)* Oh, thank you, thank you.

BADGER: I know of a secret passageway, a tunnel built many
years ago. Even Toad doesn't know about it.

RAT: Mole, draw your weapon. Badger, lead the way.

BADGER: It starts here. *(Points to an aisle or a row of seats.)*
Under this brush. Mole, being the weakest, you bring up the
rear.

MOLE: But I can fight!

BADGER: Yes, but I am in command. *(THEY crawl single file
down the aisle or between the seats until BADGER stops
abruptly.)*

RAT: What's up?

BADGER: The tunnel has caved in. I am afraid it is no use.
We must turn back.

RAT: Every moment may be Toad's last.

MOLE: I can dig! Let me up there!

BADGER: Very well. Mole to the front. *(MOLE crawls over
and around the other two and begins to dig.)*

RAT: Hurry, hurry!

BADGER: There's no time to lose.

MOLE: We're through! I can see light up ahead. Forward!
(THEY emerge, run up onto the stage.)

TOAD: Rescued!

BADGER: Not quite. Where is the villain?

TOAD: In there. Quickly, untie me! *(THIEF ENTERS.)*
RAT: No time for that.
(THEY engage the THIEF. A great battle ensues. Each ANIMAL attacks the THIEF; MOLE with his wooden sword, RAT with his pop-gun, BADGER with his cane. As TOAD continues his speech, THEY surround the THIEF.)
TOAD: *(Over the fighting.)* Ha, HA! What a clever Toad am I! My enemies shut me up in prison, encircled by sentries, watched night and day by guards . . . I walk out through them all, by sheer ability only matched by my courage. They pursue me with engines . . . I snap my fingers at them and vanish, laughing, into space. *(THIEF is driven off.)* I am set upon by ruthless villains and trick them into my own territory where my superior tactics in summoning reinforcements outwit them and send them scurrying with tails between their legs. *(THIEF is gone.)* Ha, HA! I am the Toad, the handsome, the popular, the . . . *(He notices everyone staring at him.)* Er . . . could you perhaps untie me now?
BADGER: Now, Toady, I don't want to give you pain, after all you've been through already, but, seriously, don't you see what an awful fool you've been making of yourself? On your own admission you have been handcuffed, imprisoned, starved, chased, terrified out of your life, insulted, jeered at, bound hand and foot in your own home. Where's the amusement in that? When are you going to be sensible, and think of your friends, and try to be a credit to them?
TOAD: *(Meekly.)* Quite right, Badger. How sound you always are. Yes, I've been a conceited old fool, I can quite see that; but now I'm going to be a good Toad, and as for motorcars, I promise never to touch one again.
RAT: Hooray for Toad!
MOLE: I am so proud of you!
TOAD: Now you may release me from my bonds.
BADGER: Not yet. Not until you swear to make your promise good before all the animals of the forest.
TOAD: Must I?
BADGER: You must.
TOAD: Very well. If you will just untie my hand, I shall swear.
BADGER: Rat? *(RAT unties TOAD.)* Well?
TOAD: Couldn't you do this for me?
BADGER: No.
TOAD: I . . . swear.
BADGER: Good. I accept your word.
TOAD: I shall begin my address with a short lecture on my recent adventures followed by a question-and-answer period after which . . .

BADGER: No. No speeches. Just your solemn promise to reform.

TOAD: Mayn't I sing them one little song?

BADGER: No, not one little song. It's no good, Toady; you know well that your songs are all conceit and boasting and vanity and . . .

MOLE: And gas.

BADGER: Thank you, Mole.

RAT: It's for your own good, Toady. You know you must turn over a new leaf sooner or later and now seems a splendid time to begin. Please don't think that saying all this doesn't hurt us more than it hurts you. Your friends are your friends for what you are, not what you do.

TOAD: Henceforth I will be a very different Toad. My friends, you shall never have occasion to blush for me again. But, oh, dear, oh, dear, this is a hard world!

BADGER: Attention, all animals of the forest! Toad is going to make an important declaration, and I want you all to listen carefully, for you may never hear its like again. *(BADGER, MOLE and RAT go among the Audience, inviting the animals to hear TOAD, thanking them for their help, etc.)*

BADGER: Toad?

TOAD: Ahem. My friends. I, the great and . . . the . . . that is, I, Mister Toad of . . . . I, uh, I asked Badger to ask you all here . . . or rather he asked me to ask you . . . oh, this is terribly difficult. You see, I am not the same Toad you have all known and admired, er, all known and respected, er, all known. No, indeed, no. In fact, just the other day when I was cleverly outwitting . . . when I was . . . well, I thought to myself, perhaps I was wr-o-o-o- . . . or, to put it another way, maybe I have been a f-f-f-oo-oo- . . . *(He is interrupted by the sound of a motor overhead.)*

MOLE: Whatever can that be?

RAT: A motorcar that flies?

BADGER: No, no. I have heard of such contraptions. It is an aeroplane.

TOAD: *(Eyes bulging.)* Aer-o-plane!

BADGER: *(TOAD starts OFF.)* Toad, come back. After him!

TOAD: *(Pretending to be a plane, his arms the wings.)* Putt-putt! Putt-putt! Zoo-oo-oom!

RAT: Here we go again.

MOLE: Hooray! *(THEY chase TOAD around and OFF.)*

THE END

PRODUCTION NOTES

SET: The play takes place in the year 1910 in a quiet country-side. In order to expedite the flow of the action, set changes should be kept to a minimum. Scenes will be established primarily by props carried on and off by the characters. An all-purpose, woodsy setting is suggested, with several variously-shaped blocks that can double as rocks, chairs, the Judge's bench, etc. These may have hidden compartments in which props can be stored for use in different scenes; for example, a tea kettle for Rat's House, or a justice scale for the Court. The use of lighting to vary the ambience of each scene, such as making the Wild Wood dark and foreboding, would be very effective.

VEHICLES: The play calls for several vehicles which must be ridden by the characters. It is suggested that actual moving vehicles NOT be used. Instead they may be represented in one of two ways. First, by using the set pieces described above and having the actors mime the motion of each vehicle, perhaps with the addition of props such as a buggy-whip, a steering wheel, an air horn, a bell and the like. In this case, sound effects would be particularly useful; a horse's whinny and hoof-beats, a motor-car, a railway train.

Second, in proscenium productions especially, each vehicle can be a cut-out flat which the actors can get "in" or behind, and move across the stage by sliding or carrying.

SOUND: The music may be augmented by instruments of a chordal or rhythmic nature, especially if used on stage. In Scene Two, for example, Rat might strum a banjo, and Toad could have a tambourine when he returns. At the very least, a real flute or recorder should be heard offstage in Scene Nine, if at all possible. Talented actors may comprise the entire orchestra, as one or more of them is off stage during every musical number.

Sound effects will enhance the production greatly, especially to establish the vehicles. Note in particular the sound of a motor-car in Scene Two and the sound of an airplane in Scene Eleven (which may be the same sound) are essential. If stereo speakers are used, the sound can be heard to move from one side of the stage to the other.

Other sounds such as the sounds of the forest (chirps, hoots, whistles, etc.) and the sounds of the prison guards should be done "live" by the off stage actors.

PARTICIPATION: In several key scenes, the play may be opened up for participation by the audience. As noted in the script, the aisles may be used for part of the action. However, audience members should NOT be encouraged to leave their seats or get on stage as this would impede the progress of the play. Nor is it essential to depend on audience participation to continue with the play.

COSTUMES: Dress should reflect the period, circa 1910, or at least a hazy yesteryear. The animals (Toad, Rat, Mole and Badget) should be seen as very human, but judicious use of make-up to imply each animal's attributes (whiskers, etc.) is permissible. The humans, (Judge, Washerwoman, Engineer, Thief) especially if played by the same actor, may very effectively be masked to infer the sameness of people as seen by animals.

The following costumes are merely suggestions:
MOLE: Knee-pants, beanie plus Scene Five - mittens, earmuffs, muffler.
RAT: Nautical blazer, bosun's shirt, captain's cap, ascot.
BADGER: Crooked top hat and tails, cane, wire-rim eyeglasses.
TOAD: Spats, sporty vest, loud jacket, bow tie, straw hat; plus Scene Two - bandana; Scene Three - Motorist's duster and cap, goggles; Scene Four - handcuffs; Scene Six Striped prison shirt, woman's dress, shawl and bonnet (all worn over basic costume).
JUDGE: Black robe, white wig.
WASHERWOMAN: Long dress, apron, bonnet.
ENGINEER: Striped overalls, cap, red kerchief.
THIEF: Black cape, ruffled shirt, boots, feathered hat, rapier.

PROPS:
MOLE: Spyglass, wooden sword, button
RAT: Picnic basket, compass, steering wheel, tea kettle, backpack, pop-gun.
BADGER: Walking stick
TOAD: Wet handkerchief, buggy whip, bandana, goggles, handcuffs, ball and chain
JUDGE: Gavel, scales of justice
WASHERWOMAN: Laundry basket filled with clothes, key
ENGINEER: Oil can
THIEF: Union card, pot, rope, pelts, sword

Make Your Play
A Lasting Memory With
Theatre Shirts

The Wonderful
Wizard
Of Oz

RHS
Drama Club
Presents

- T-shirts, long-sleeved t-shirts and sweat shirts are now available for ALL of your favorite PIONEER PLAYS.

- Create team spirit while you publicize your play!

- Personalize shirts for cast, crew, band, directors, even parents!

- Customize your shirts by:
    Selecting from a variety of fabric colors
    Selecting from a variety of ink colors
    .... of your organization
    .... uction dates

Wind in the Willows

.... director or contact
.... vice, Inc. for more details!